A DAY IN THE LIFE OF

By Arelis Gomes & Jaylen Gomes
Illustrated by Jason Velazquez

A Day In The Life of Jaylen
© 2020 by Arelis Gomes and Jaylen Gomes
Illustrated by Jason Velazquez

Printed in the United States of America.
ISBN-13: 978-1-7353705-7-6

Jaylen's House Books
Brockton. MA

JAYLEN'S HOUSE
BOOKS

This book is dedicated to all the beautiful children on the Autism spectrum. Remember being different is what makes people unique and great.

Jaylen's House books will educate the world about Autism. All children on the Autism spectrum will now have a character in a book that they can identify with and see first hand that all things are possible and no matter the challenges and circumstances they face they can and will succeed.

My name is Jaylen.

I have Autism.

I am unable to speak.

Sometimes I laugh.

Sometimes I cover my ears to block loud noise.

Sometimes I walk
back and forth.

EEEEEEEEEEH!

Sometimes I jump.

Sometimes I cry.

Sometimes I wave.

Sometimes I dance.

This is my way of speaking.

When I look at you with my Big Brown eyes and smile...

That is all I need to do.

This is my way of speaking to you.